HEINEMANN MATHEMATICS 1

Name

WORKBOOK 2
Counting to 5

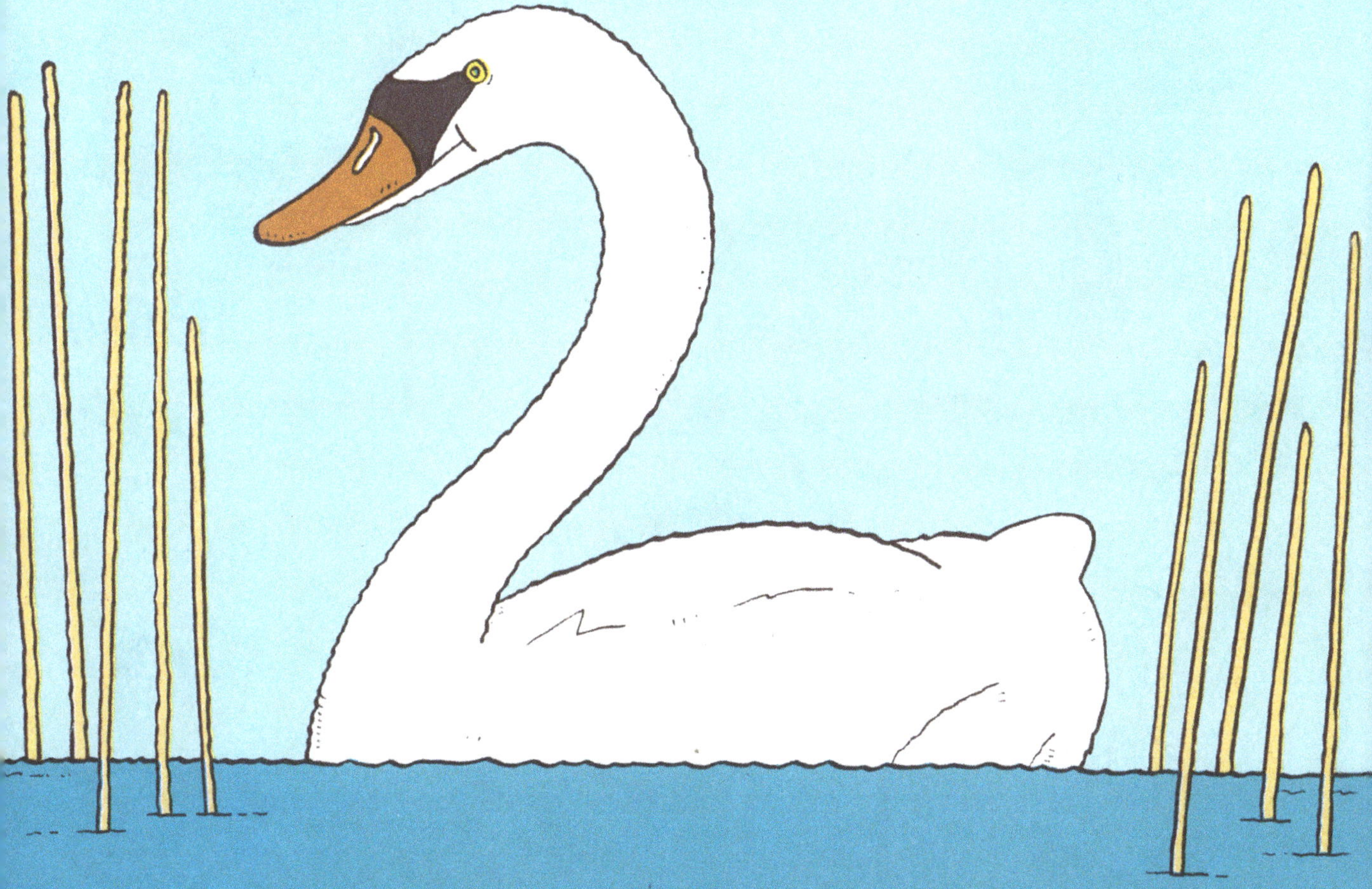

Revised

Sets of 1

Write 1

tree   house

car

flower   girl

Write 2

2 2 2 2 2 2
2

cows
sheep
hens
ducks
rabbits

3 3 ˙ ˙ ˙ ˙

Draw 1 more. How many now?

Draw

Write 1 or 2 or 3.

Counting to 4

4 4 ′ ′ ′ ′

Draw 1 more. How many now?

☐

☐

☐

☐

Draw

4 fish

4 ducks

4 boats

4 soaps

Colour

Colour 4 green.

Colour 4 red.

Colour 4 blue.   **Colour 4 green.**

Ordering

Write 1, 2, 3 or 4.

Counting to 5

5 5

Draw 1 more. How many now?

Draw sweets 🟢.

Counting to 5

Draw 5 spots on each dog.

How many girls?

How many dogs?

How many?

bands

rings

balls

skittles

hoops

shoes

Counting to 5

15

How many eggs?

Draw the missing eggs.

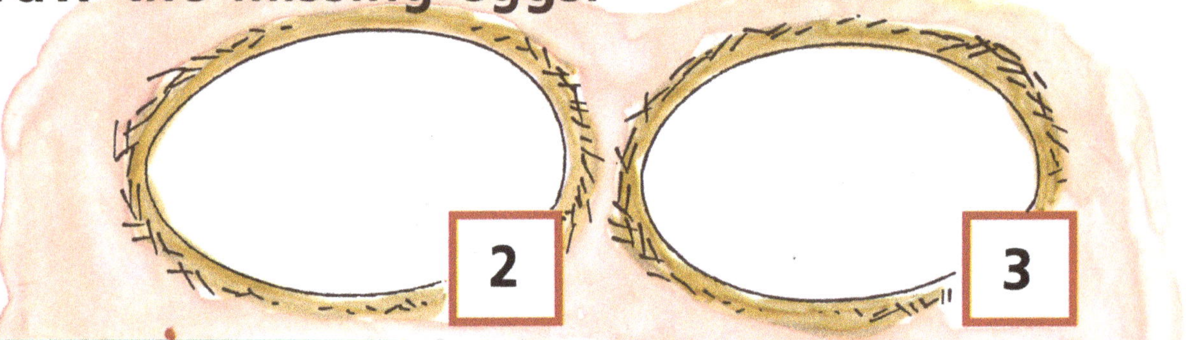

2

3

Extension

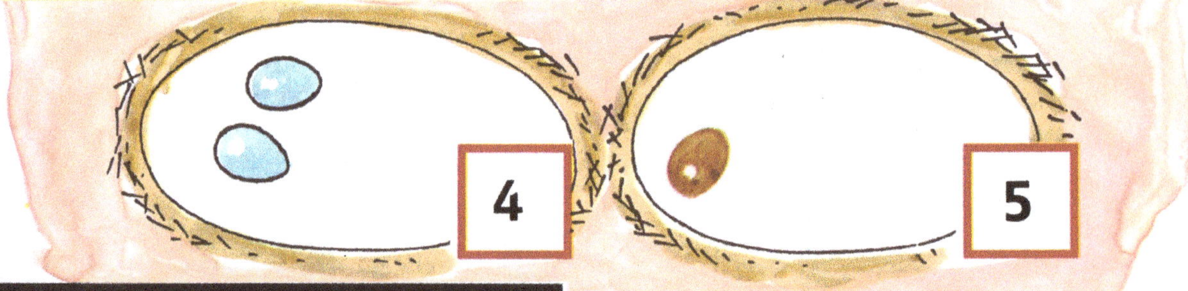

4

5

CARDS Counting to 5 Cards 1 to 7

1	2	3	4	5	6	7	8	9	10	11	12	13	14	15

Heinemann is an imprint of Pearson Education Limited, a company incorporated in England and Wales, having its registered office at Edinburgh Gate, Harlow, Essex, CM20 2JE.
Registered company number: 872828
ISBN 978 0 435 03083 4 © Scottish Primary Mathematics Group 1991.
First published 1991. Revised edition 1995.   2024   27
Typeset and illustrated by Oxprint Design. Printed and bound by Ashford Colour Press Ltd

ISBN 978-0-435030-83-4